General instructions

CW00538006

This book contains the following three practice papers.

- Maths Paper 1: arithmetic (30 minutes)
- Maths Paper 2: reasoning (40 minutes)
- Maths Paper 3: reasoning (40 minutes)

It is best to do the papers in the order they appear in the book, but don't do all the tests at the same time. Have a break between tests.

Before you start a test

When you are ready to do one of the practice papers, find a quiet place where you can concentrate.

Make sure you have enough time to complete the practice paper before you start it. Use a watch or clock to check the time or ask an adult to time the test for you.

When you are ready to begin, turn to the first page of the practice paper and start timing the test.

During Maths Paper 1

Work through the test on your own.

You do not have to show your working out if you can do it mentally, but for the two-mark questions at the end you could score a mark for your working, even if you get the final answer wrong. Stop at the end of the test. This is clearly marked 'End of test'. If you have time, go back and check your work.

During Maths Papers 2 and 3

Work through the test on your own.

Follow the instructions carefully for each question. If you need to do any working out, you can use any space on a page. Stop at the end of the test. This is clearly marked 'End of test'. If you have time, go back and check your work.

The numbers in the right-hand margin of each test page tell you how many marks each question is worth. Don't look at the answers before or during the test.

After the test

Ask an adult to mark your practice paper using the answers and mark scheme on pages 47–54. Record your score in the boxes on pages 3 and 55.

Look at any questions you couldn't do or answered incorrectly. These are topics you need to revise. The Schofield & Sims **Key Stage 2 Maths Revision Guide** will help you with this.

**DO NOT TURN OVER THIS PAGE UNTIL YOU ARE
READY TO START PAPER 1: ARITHMETIC.**

Paper 1: arithmetic

Instructions

You are **not** allowed to use a calculator to answer any questions in this test.

Work carefully and quickly.

You have **30 minutes** to do Paper 1: arithmetic.

If you cannot do a question, go on to the next one. If you have time, you can come back to it later.

If you have time, go back and check your work.

> **Follow the instructions carefully for each question.**
>
> For each question, write your answer in the red box.
>
> You do not have to show your working out if you can do it mentally, but for the two-mark questions at the end you should show your method. You could score a mark for your working, even if you get the final answer wrong. You can use the squared grids for your working out.

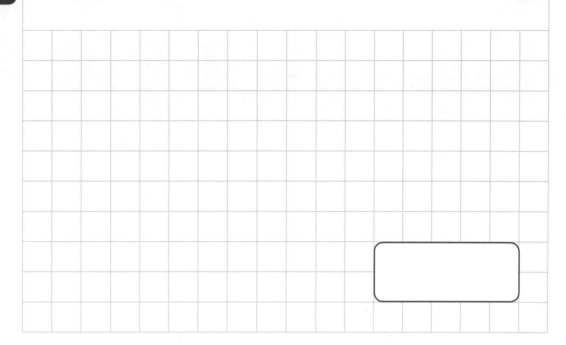

1 8604 − 173 =

1 mark

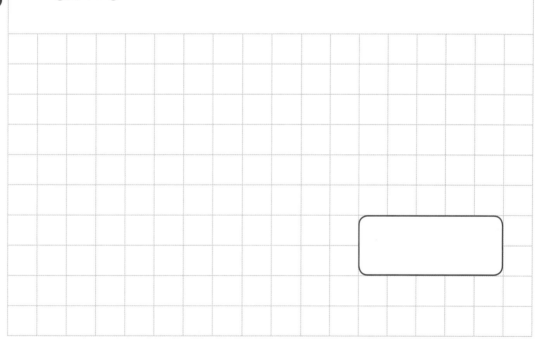

2 32 × 5 =

1 mark

page 7
total

please turn over

Revision Guide links
If you need help with this topic after your test has been
marked, read the following pages in the Revision Guide:
Question 1 pages 33, 35   Question 2 pages 41, 43

3   879 − 587 =

1 ma

4 $5^2 =$

1 ma

5 $2\frac{3}{7} - \frac{5}{7} =$

1 mar

6 $\frac{1}{2} \times \frac{3}{4} =$

1 mark

7 $100 + 20 \times 3 =$

1 mark

please turn over

pages
8–9
total

Revision Guide links

If you need help with this topic after your test has been marked, read the following pages in the Revision Guide:

Question 3 pages 33, 35 Question 4 page 38

Question 5 pages 19, 21 Question 6 page 22

Question 7 pages 33, 41, 45

8   3.7 + 0.09 =

1 ma

9   1320 ÷ 11 =

1 ma

10   [   ] – 684 = 8684

1 mar

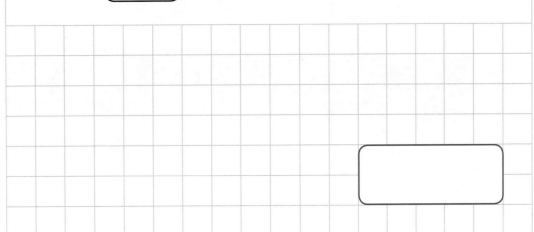

11   $10 \times \boxed{} = 1200$

1 mark

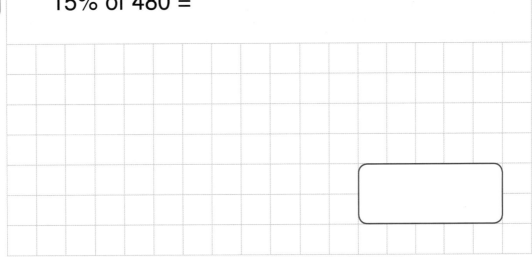

12   15% of 480 =

1 mark

please turn over

Revision Guide links
If you need help with this topic after your test has been
marked, read the following pages in the Revision Guide:
Question 8 page 34   Question 9 pages 42, 44
Question 10 pages 33, 35, 48   Question 11 pages 41, 43, 48
Question 12 pages 28, 30

Schofield & Sims • Key Stage 2 **Maths Practice Papers**

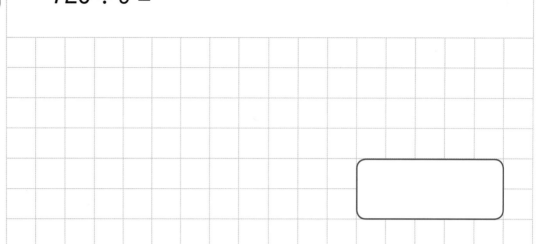

13 720 ÷ 9 =

1 m

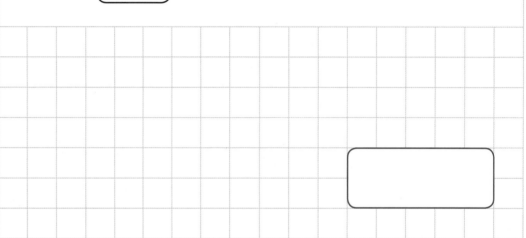

14 91 ÷ ⬚ = 0.091

1 mc

15   7% of 900 =

1 mark

16   243 × 6 =

1 mark

please turn over

Revision Guide links
If you need help with this topic after your test has been
marked, read the following pages in the Revision Guide:
Question 13 pages 42, 44   Question 14 pages 42, 48
Question 15 pages 28, 30   Question 16 pages 41, 43

17   1632 ÷ 4 =

1 m

18   1.46 × 8 =

1 ma

19   1741 × 7 =

1 mark

20   1155 ÷ 3 =

1 mark

Revision Guide links
If you need help with this topic after your test has been
marked, read the following pages in the Revision Guide:
Question 17 pages 42, 44   Question 18 pages 41, 43
Question 19 pages 41, 43   Question 20 pages 42, 44

please turn over

pages
14–15
total

Schofield & Sims • Key Stage 2 **Maths Practice Papers**

15

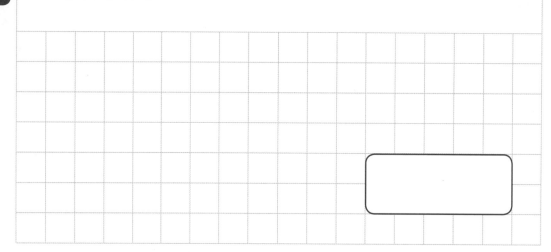

21   $5 \times 6 \times 8 =$

1 m

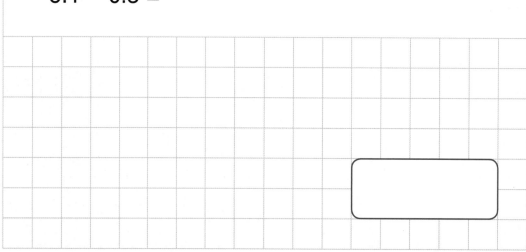

22   $6.1 - 0.3 =$

1 m

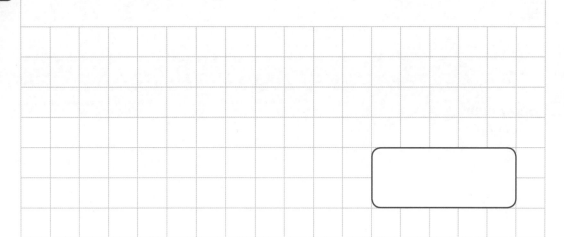

23   15 − 7.01 =

1 mark

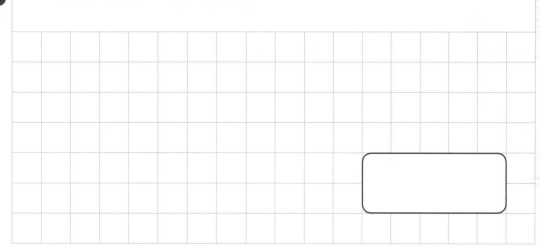

24   274 385 − 35 998 =

1 mark

pages
16–17
total

please turn over

Revision Guide links
If you need help with this topic after your test has been
marked, read the following pages in the Revision Guide:
Question 21 pages 41, 43   Question 22 page 35
Question 23 page 35   Question 24 pages 33, 35

Schofield & Sims • Key Stage 2 **Maths Practice Papers**   17

25

$$\begin{array}{r} 2\ 8 \\ \times\quad 1\ 4 \\ \hline \end{array}$$

Show your method

2 ma

26

17) 1 8 1 9

Show your method

2 ma

27 $15 \times 1\frac{1}{2} =$

1 mark

28 $\frac{3}{4} \div 2 =$

1 mark

29 $\frac{3}{7} + \frac{2}{7} =$

1 mark

pages
18–19
total

please turn over

Revision Guide links
If you need help with this topic after your test has been
marked, read the following pages in the Revision Guide:
Question 25 page 43   Question 26 page 44
Question 27 pages 22, 41, 43   Question 28 page 22
Question 29 page 21

30

$$\begin{array}{r} 4\ 1\ 0\ 8 \\ \times \qquad 3\ 6 \\ \hline \end{array}$$

Show your method

2 marks

31

6 4 | 7 0 4 0

Show your method

2 marks

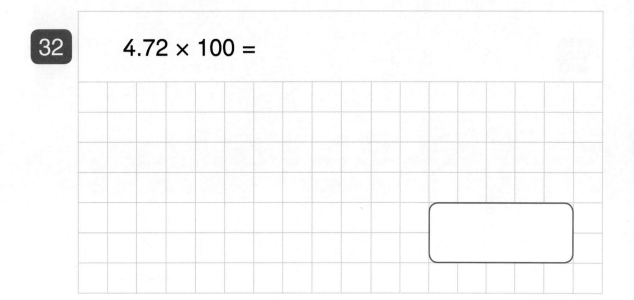

32 | $4.72 \times 100 =$

1 mark

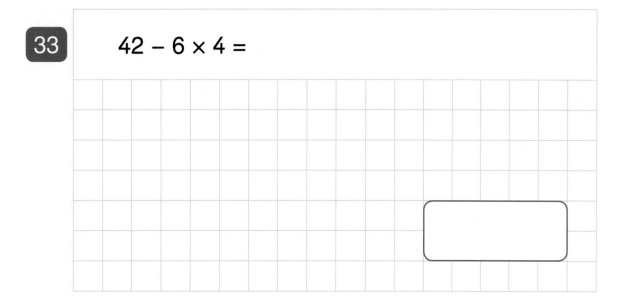

33 | $42 - 6 \times 4 =$

1 mark

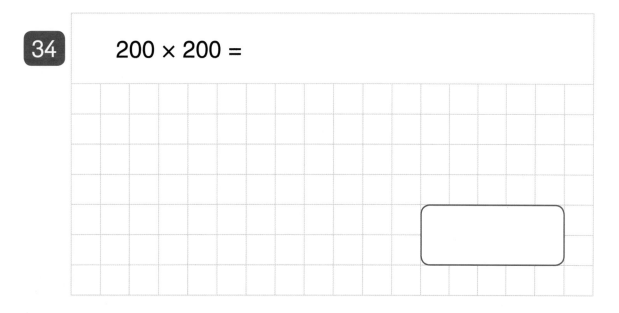

34 | $200 \times 200 =$

1 mark

pages
20–21
total

please turn over

Revision Guide links
If you need help with this topic after your test has been
marked, read the following pages in the Revision Guide:
Question 30 page 43   Question 31 page 44
Question 32 pages 41, 43   Question 33 pages 39, 45
Question 34 pages 41, 43

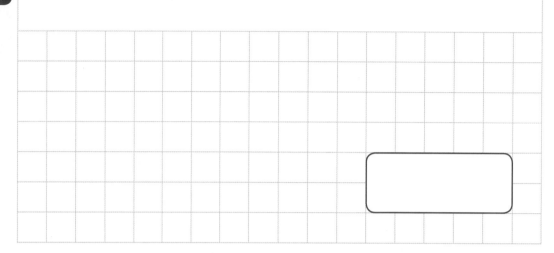

35 16.7 – 8.78 =

1 ma

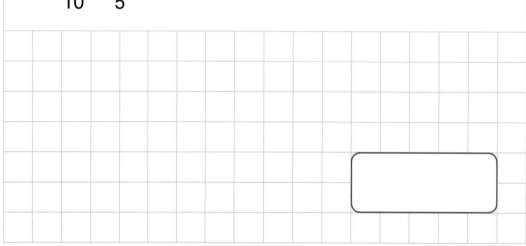

36 $1\frac{1}{10} \times \frac{2}{5} =$

1 ma

END OF TEST

page
total

**Total score
for Paper 1**
Write this score in the box
on pages 3 and 55.

Revision Guide links
If you need help with this topic after your test
has been marked, read the following pages in
the Revision Guide:
Question 35 page 35   Question 36 page 22

Paper 2: reasoning

Instructions

You are **not** allowed to use a calculator to answer any questions in this test.

Work carefully and quickly.

You have **40 minutes** to do Paper 2: reasoning.

If you cannot do a question, go on to the next one. If you have time, you can come back to it later.

If you have time, go back and check your work.

Follow the instructions carefully for each question.

If you need to do any working out, you can use any space on the page.

**DO NOT TURN OVER THIS PAGE UNTIL YOU ARE
READY TO START PAPER 2: REASONING**

A shop sells different bottles of drinks.

This table shows the most popular drinks sold in the shop during one week.

Drink	Large	Regular
blackcurrant	12	15
orange	14	12
lemon	11	18

How many **large** bottles of **orange** were sold during the week?

1 mc

Which flavour sold most bottles during the week?

1 mc

2 Draw a circle around all the numbers that give an answer of 36 000 when **rounded** to the nearest 1000.

1 mc

36 700   37 666   35 901

         36 196   35 099

3 Jack's dad is weighing his dogs for the Dog Show.

Tilly   Jess   Buster

Jess weighs $12\frac{1}{2}$kg. Buster weighs twice as much.

How much does Buster weigh?

[____ kg]

1 mark

The three dogs together weigh exactly 50kg.

How much does Tilly weigh?

[____ kg]

1 mark

4 Deepa is describing one of the statements below.

Six more than 'three lots of P' equals twelve

Circle the statement that she is describing.

$6 + 3 + P = 17$ $9P = 12$

$6 + 3P = 12$ $6P + 3 = 12$

1 mark

pages
24–25
total

Revision Guide links
If you need help with this topic after your test has been
marked, read the following pages in the Revision Guide:
Question 1 page 83   Question 2 pages 6–7
Question 3a pages 41, 50   Question 3b page 33
Question 4 pages 50–51

please turn over

5 Draw an arrow on this scale to show 775g.

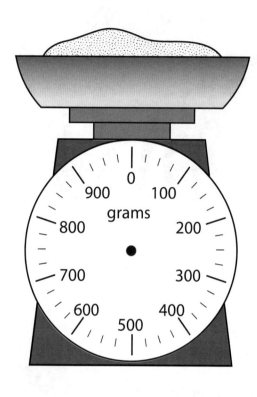

How many more grams is 3 kilograms than 775g?

g

1 m

6 Oscar correctly wrote the number 587 using Roman numerals.

Circle the number that Oscar wrote.

XXXVII   LXXXIIX   DXXXVII

DLXXXVII   CCCCCXXIIIX

1 ma

7 Here is a multiplication fact.

$$37 \times 91 = 3367$$

Use this multiplication fact to answer these questions.

$370 \times 91 =$

1 mark

$37 \times 9.1 =$

1 mark

$37 \times 92 =$

1 mark

8 Write these proportions in order, starting with the **smallest**.

75% $\dfrac{2}{3}$ 0.7 $\dfrac{1}{10}$ 60%

1 mark

Revision Guide links
If you need help with this topic after your test has been marked, read the following pages in the Revision Guide:
Question 5 page 62   Question 6 page 16
Question 7a, 7b page 4   Question 7c page 39
Question 8 pages 8, 26–27, 30

please turn over

9 Here is a map of the inside of a leisure centre.

Not to scale

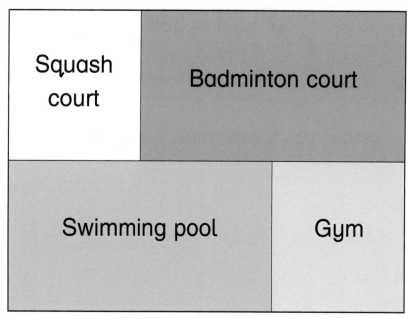

Approximately what **fraction** of the area of the leisure centre does the swimming pool cover?

The leisure centre is a rectangle, where the longer side is twice the length of the shorter side. The **shorter** side of the rectangle is **25m**.

What is the **perimeter** of the leisure centre?

m

1 mark

10 **Two-fifths** of a pizza is cut into **four** equal slices.

What **fraction** of the whole pizza is each new slice? Give your answer in its simplest form.

1 mark

11 Draw and shade the reflection of this shape in the mirror line.

Use a ruler.

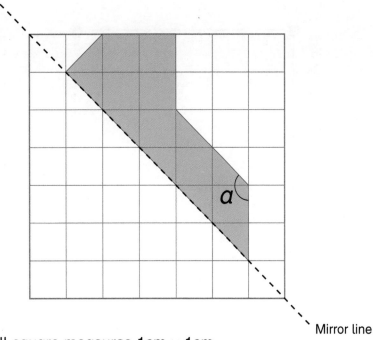

Mirror line

Each small square measures 1cm × 1cm.

1 mark

What **area** of the grid is now shaded?

cm²

1 mark

What **fraction** of the grid is now shaded?

1 mark

How many **degrees** is angle *a*?

°

1 mark

You may use a protractor.

Revision Guide links
If you need help with this topic after your test has been marked, read the following pages in the Revision Guide:
Question 9a pages 17–18   Question 9b pages 55–56
Question 10 page 22
Question 11a page 72   Question 11b pages 57–58
Question 11c pages 17–18   Question 11d pages 77–80

pages
28–29
total

please turn over

12 Fill in the missing **co-ordinates** of points **C** and **D**.

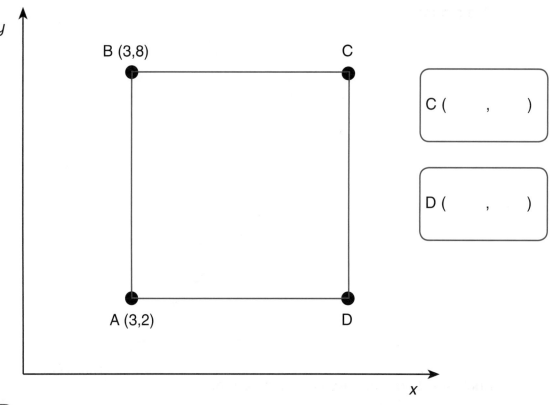

C (,   )

1 ma

D (,   )

13 Ava has some cut-out paper polygons.

Name shape C.

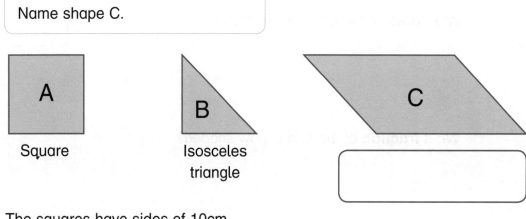

Square   Isosceles
triangle

1 ma

The squares have sides of 10cm.

Calculate the total **area** of the six shapes below.

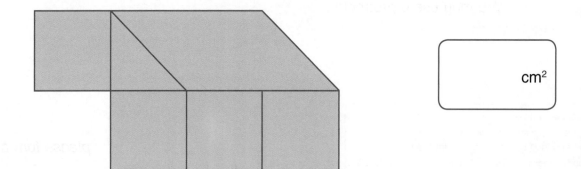

cm²

1 ma

14 This table shows what six children had in their pencil cases.

Name	Ruler	Pencil	Rubber	Pen
Sanjay	0	3	1	2
Adam	1	1	2	0
James	0	0	2	3
Ella	0	1	1	1
Sam	1	2	0	2
Rose	1	3	1	0

Who had the most items in their pencil case?

1 mark

This graph shows what **five** of the children had in their pencil cases.

One child's information has been left off the chart.

A bar chart to show the items in six children's pencil cases

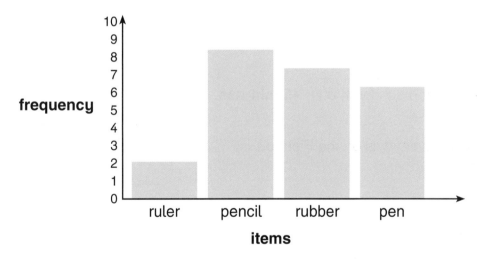

Which child's information has been missed off the chart? Explain how you know this.

....

....

1 mark

pages
30–31
total

Revision Guide links
If you need help with this topic after your test has been
marked, read the following pages in the Revision Guide:
Question 12 pages 74–76   Question 13 pages 57–58
Question 14 page 83

please turn over

15 Here is the programme of events in an athletics competition.

Programme of events		
Time	**Track**	**Field**
7.00	Men's 5000 metres	Women's high jump
7.30	Women's 5000 metres	Men's javelin
8.00	Women's 10 000 metres	↓
8.30	↓	Women's pole vault
9.00	Men's 100 metres	Men's high jump
9.30	Women's 100 metres	Women's javelin

Josh arrived at **twenty-five to eight**.

What event was on the Track at that time?

1 mark

He left for a sandwich after **45 minutes**.

What event was on the Field at that time?

1 mark

16 Calculate the size of the missing **angles** in each polygon.

Do **not** use a protractor.

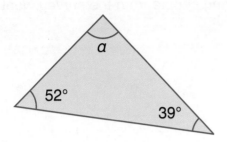

$a =$ ⬚ °

1 mark

$b =$ ⬚ °

1 mark

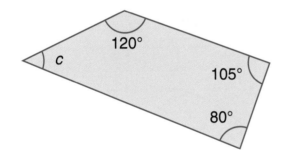

$c =$ ⬚ °

1 mark

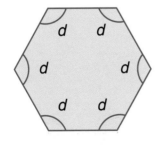

$d =$ ⬚ °

1 mark

pages
32–33
total

please turn over

Revision Guide links
If you need help with this topic after your test has been
marked, read the following pages in the Revision Guide:
Question 15 pages 64–66   Question 16 pages 80–81

17 48 people went on holiday last summer.

This pie chart shows that twice as many people went to Greece as went to Portugal, and the same number went to Portugal as went to the USA.

Complete the table to show how many people from the survey went to each place.

Country	Number of people
USA	
Spain	
Greece	
Portugal	
France	

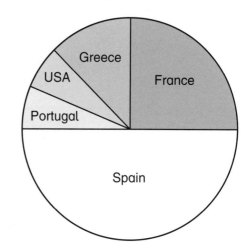

2 marks

This table shows the favourite cities of 36 people.

Complete the pie chart below to show this data.

Use a protractor.

City	Number of people
London	9
Paris	12
Rome	6
Athens	5
New York	4

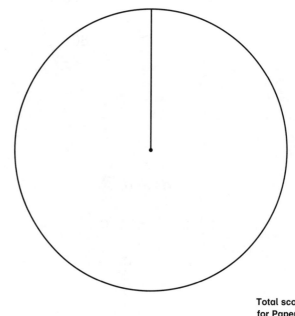

2 marks

page 3 total

END OF TEST

Total score
for Paper 2
Write this score in the box
on pages 3 and 55.

Revision Guide links
If you need help with this topic after your test
has been marked, read the following pages in
the Revision Guide: Question 17 pages 86–87

Paper 3: reasoning

Instructions

You are **not** allowed to use a calculator to answer any questions in this test.

Work carefully and quickly.

You have **40 minutes** to do Paper 3: reasoning.

If you cannot do a question, go on to the next one. If you have time, you can come back to it later.

If you have time, go back and check your work.

> **Follow the instructions carefully for each question.**
>
> If you need to do any working out, you can use any space on the page.

**DO NOT TURN OVER THIS PAGE UNTIL YOU ARE
READY TO START PAPER 3: REASONING**

1 How many cubes is this cuboid made from?

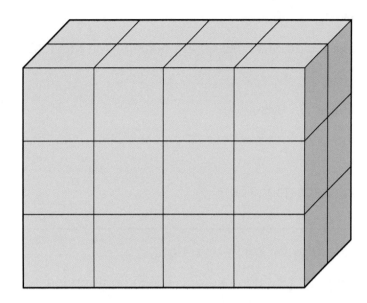

1 mc

2 Lauren takes two maths tests.

In Test 1 she scores 50 out of 80 and in Test 2 she scores 26 out of 40.

Write both scores as **percentages**.

Lauren's score
for Test 1

Lauren's score
for Test 2

1 mc

3 Put these numbers in order of size, starting with the **smallest**.

 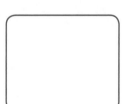  

3.4   3.14   3.42   3.146

1 ma

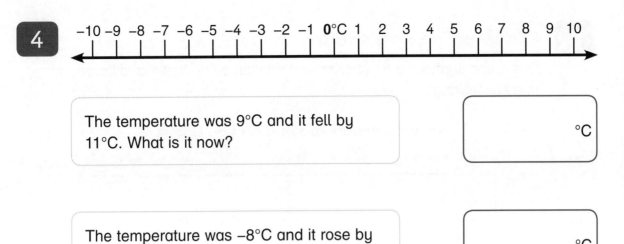

4

The temperature was 9°C and it fell by 11°C. What is it now?

°C

1 mark

The temperature was −8°C and it rose by 12°C. What is it now?

°C

1 mark

5

Sophie has saved £74.86 and has a voucher for £5. How much more does she need to buy a camera costing £87.49?

Show your method.

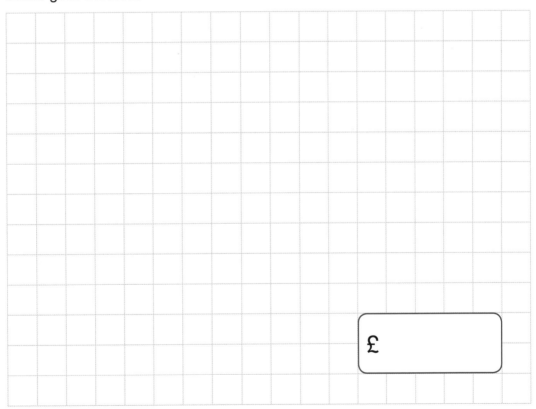

£

2 marks

pages
36–37
total

please turn over

Revision Guide links

If you need help with this topic after your test has been marked, read the following pages in the Revision Guide:

Question 1 page 60   Question 2 pages 26–27

Question 3 pages 23–24   Question 4 pages 9–11

Question 5 pages 34–35, 46

Whitborough Castle is a tourist attraction.

This graph shows the number of visitors inside the castle at different times yesterday.

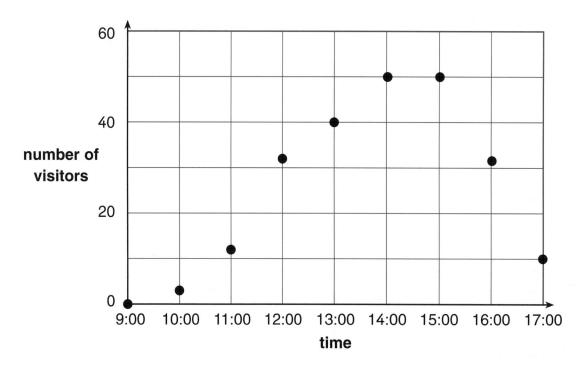

What was the approximate number of visitors at 12:00?

1 mc

How many more visitors were in the castle at 12:00 than at 17:00?

1 mc

Could there have been more than 50 visitors in the castle at any time? Explain your answer.

....

....

....

1 ma

7

Birdseed costs £2.50 for 1kg.

Ryan buys 400 grams of birdseed.

How much does he pay?	£

1 mark

Dog biscuits cost £4.80 for 1kg.

Jennie buys a bag of dog biscuits for 60p.

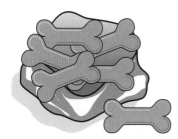

How many grams of dog biscuits are in the bag?

Show your method.

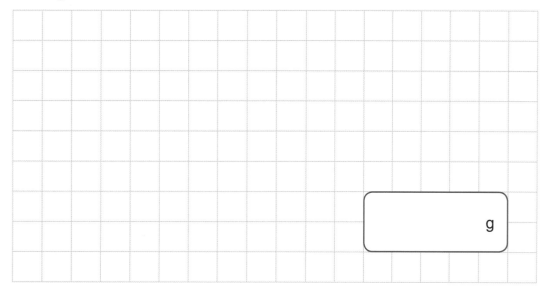

g

2 marks

pages
38–39
total

please turn over

Revision Guide links

If you need help with this topic after your test has been marked, read the following pages in the Revision Guide:

Question 6 page 85

Question 7a pages 19–20, 22, 46

Question 7b pages 19–20, 22, 43–44, 46

8 Dan mixes every 3 tins of red paint with 1 tin of white.

He uses 16 tins of paint altogether.

How many of these are red?

1 mc

Yesterday Dan mixed tins of paint in the ratio 2 white tins to every 5 red tins. He used 8 tins of white paint.

How many tins of paint did he mix altogether?

1 mo

9 A circle has a radius of 10.4 cm.

Write the length of its diameter.  cm

1 mo

10 Fill in the missing digit to make this statement true.

$$\frac{\boxed{}}{5} \times \boxed{3} = \boxed{1}\frac{\boxed{4}}{5}$$

1 ma

11 Write the answer for each puzzle in the box.

I'm thinking of a number less than 20.

It is a factor of 108.

It is a multiple of 3.

It is a square number.

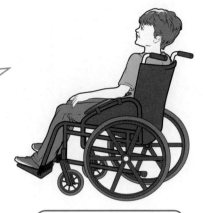

1 mark

I'm thinking of a number between 10 and 30.

It is a prime number.

The sum of its digits is 5.

1 mark

12 A and B each stand for a whole number.

A is four times as big as B.

A plus B equals 80.

Find the values of A and B.

A =

B =

1 mark

pages
40–41
total

please turn over

Revision Guide links

If you need help with this topic after your test has been
marked, read the following pages in the Revision Guide:

Question 8 pages 31–32   Question 9 page 82

Question 10 pages 22, 48   Question 11 pages 36–38

Question 12 pages 31–32, 50–51

Schofield & Sims • Key Stage 2 **Maths Practice Papers**   41

13 Vishal uses **four** number cards to make different fractions.

All the fractions he makes are less than 1.

| 6 | 3 | 9 | 2 |

> Show where each number card would go to make this statement correct.
>
> Use each number card only **once.**

$$\frac{\boxed{}}{\boxed{}} \quad \text{is equivalent to} \quad \frac{\boxed{}}{\boxed{}}$$

1 mark

14 This sequence increases in **equal sized** steps.

> Fill in the missing numbers.

| 7 | | | | 39 |

1 mark

15 One of these cards is face down. The mean of the five numbers is 7.

| 6 | 4 | 7 | 9 | |

What is the number on the fifth card?

1 mark

16 Look at this co-ordinate grid.

Give the co-ordinates of point A.

(,   )

1 mark

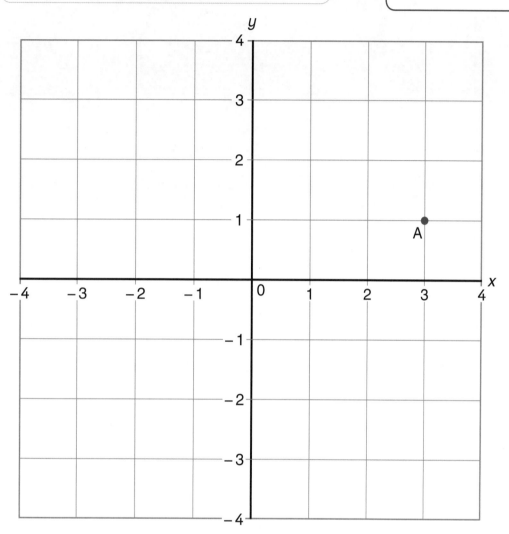

Draw point B at **(–3,2)**.

1 mark

Revision Guide links
If you need help with this topic after your test has been
marked, read the following pages in the Revision Guide:
Question 13 page 18   Question 14 pages 12–13
Question 15 page 89   Question 16 pages 74–75

pages
42–43
total

please turn over

17 Look at the shapes on the grid.

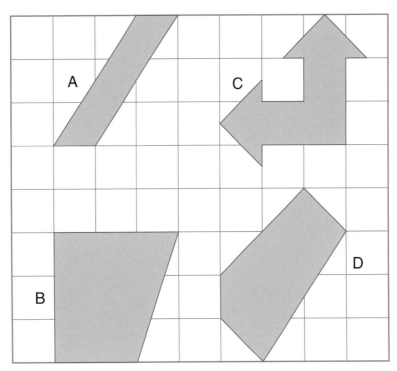

Write **one** of the letters into each sentence below to make it correct.

Shape ☐ is a pentagon.

1 m

Shape ☐ is a parallelogram.

1 m

Shape ☐ has reflective symmetry.

1 m

18 Matthew has £y.

He spends £9.

Write an **expression** to show how many pounds he has now.

1 m

19 Lucy spent an afternoon at the theme park.

Rides	
Laser	£2.60
Mars	£1.25
Star	£3.00

She went on all the rides and paid **£14.55** in total. This included three rides on the Laser.

How many times did she go on the Mars ride?

1 mark

20 What missing numbers make these statements correct?

In each statement, all the numbers should be **different**.

$$4 \quad \times \quad \boxed{} \quad \times \quad \boxed{} \quad = \quad 192$$

1 mark

$$\boxed{} \quad \div \quad \boxed{} \quad = \quad 49 \quad \div \quad 7$$

1 mark

$$-27 \quad + \quad 43 \quad - \quad \boxed{} \quad = \quad 6 \quad \times \quad \boxed{}$$

1 mark

Revision Guide links

If you need help with this topic after your test has been marked, read the following pages in the Revision Guide:

Question 17 pages 67–69, 72 Question 18 pages 50–51
Question 19 page 46 Question 20a pages 41, 43, 48–49
Question 20b pages 42, 44, 48–49 Question 20c pages 10–11, 48–49

pages
44–45
total

please turn over

21 These rectangular paving slabs surround a pond.

All the paving slabs are identical in size and shape.

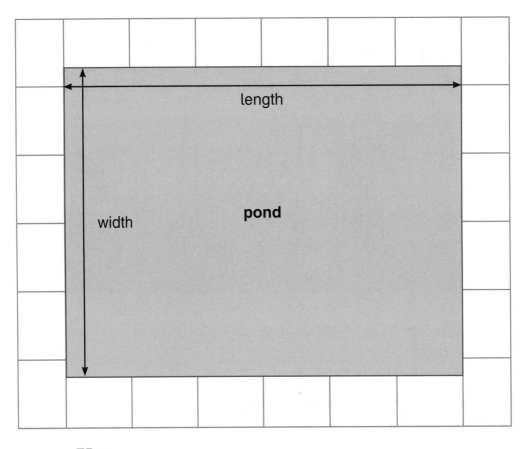

75cm

55cm

This shows the length and width of one paving slab.

Calculate the length and width of the pond in metres.

length [ ] m

width [ ] m

1 m

1 m

page
to

**Total score
for Paper 3**
Write this score in the box
on pages 3 and 55.

Revision Guide links
If you need help with this topic after your test
has been marked, read the following pages in
the Revision Guide: Question 21 pages 52–53

Answers and mark scheme

Paper 1: arithmetic

Record the mark awarded for each question. Half marks cannot be awarded.

Question	Requirement	Mark	Additional guidance
1	8431	1 mark	
2	160	1 mark	
3	292	1 mark	
4	25	1 mark	
5	$1\frac{5}{7}$	1 mark	
6	$\frac{3}{8}$	1 mark	
7	160	1 mark	
8	3.79	1 mark	
9	120	1 mark	
10	9368	1 mark	
11	120	1 mark	
12	72	1 mark	
13	80	1 mark	
14	1000	1 mark	
15	63	1 mark	
16	1458	1 mark	
17	408	1 mark	
18	11.68	1 mark	
19	12 187	1 mark	
20	385	1 mark	
21	240	1 mark	
22	5.8	1 mark	
23	7.99	1 mark	
24	238 387	1 mark	
25	392	2 marks	Award 1 mark for correct method with one arithmetical error.
26	107	2 marks	Award 1 mark for correct method with one arithmetical error.

Question	Requirement	Mark	Additional guidance
27	$22\frac{1}{2}$ or 22.5	1 mark	
28	$\frac{3}{8}$	1 mark	
29	$\frac{5}{7}$	1 mark	
30	147 888	2 marks	Award 1 mark for correct method with one arithmetical error.
31	110	2 marks	Award 1 mark for correct method with one arithmetical error.
32	472	1 mark	
33	18	1 mark	
34	40 000	1 mark	
35	7.92	1 mark	
36	$\frac{11}{25}$	1 mark	

Paper 2: reasoning

Record the mark awarded for each question. Half marks cannot be awarded.

Question	Requirement	Mark	Additional guidance
1	a 14	1 mark	The child should be familiar with reading information from a simple table.
	b lemon	1 mark	The child should check the totals of each row to find which flavour sold the most.
2	36 196, 35 901	1 mark	Only these two numbers should be circled. Give no mark if fewer or more numbers are circled or if incorrect numbers are circled.
3	a 25kg	1 mark	The child should know doubles of numbers to 100 by heart and be able to deal with doubling fractions such as $\frac{1}{2}$ and $\frac{1}{4}$.
	b 12.5kg *or* $12\frac{1}{2}$kg	1 mark	The child should be using mental methods to answer this question.
4	6 + 3P = 12	1 mark	
5	a	1 mark	Encourage the child to write other values on the scale.
	b 2225g	1 mark	
6	DLXXXVII	1 mark	
7	a 33 670	1 mark	Rather than calculating the answer using a written method, encourage the child to notice that this answer is 10 times larger than the given multiplication fact. Give 1 mark for the correct answer from a different method.
	b 336.7	1 mark	Notice that the answer is 10 times smaller than the given multiplication fact. The child could check by working out an approximate answer to decide where the decimal point should go, for example **37 × 9**.1 is approximately **40 × 10 =** 400, so the answer is not 33.67 or 3.367. Give 1 mark for the correct answer from a different method.
	c 3404	1 mark	The child should notice that 37 × 92 is 37 more than 37 × 91. Ideally, they should add 37 to 3367 to get 3404. If the child finds this difficult, discuss it in a context, e.g. 37 things costing £92 each, cost £37 more than 37 things costing £91 each. A mark can be given if the correct answer was found using a different method.
8	$\frac{1}{10}$, 60%, $\frac{2}{3}$, 0.7, 75%	1 mark	

Question	Requirement	Mark	Additional guidance
9	a $\frac{1}{3}$ *or* $\frac{2}{6}$ *or* an equivalent fraction	1 mark	The leisure centre plan can be divided into six equal sections, called sixths. The swimming pool area covers two such sections (two-sixths). This fraction is equivalent to one-third.
	b 150m	1 mark	Children often confuse area and perimeter. The perimeter of a shape is the distance all the way around the edge. If the shorter side of the rectangle is 25m, then the longer side is 50m, making the perimeter 25 + 50 + 25 + 50 = 150m.
10	$\frac{1}{10}$	1 mark	
11	a	1 mark	
	b 22cm²	1 mark	The area of a shape is the number of whole squares inside the shape. In this case it is centimetre squares or cm² that are counted. If children gave the answer 25, they are counting half squares as whole squares.
	c $\frac{22}{49}$	1 mark	There should be 22 out of 49 squares shaded.
	d 135° *or* one degree either side of 135°	1 mark	A protractor is not essential for this question. Show the child that the angle is made from a right angle and half a right angle. Half a right angle is 90 ÷ 2 = 45°, thus the angle is 90 + 45 = 135°.
12	C (9,8) D (9,2)	1 mark	Both co-ordinates must be correct to earn the mark.
13	a parallelogram	1 mark	
	b 650cm²	1 mark	
14	a Sanjay	1 mark	
	b Sam *and* a valid explanation of how they knew this.	1 mark	The explanation should indicate some understanding that the totals of each column in the table are not the same as those in the bar chart. The child might list that 1 ruler, 2 pencils and 2 pens are missing, which is what Sam had in her/his pencil case. Any acceptable explanation with a correct answer scores 1 mark.

Question	Requirement		Mark	Additional guidance
15	**a** Women's 5000 metres		1 mark	
	b Men's javelin		1 mark	If the child incorrectly answered Women's 10 000m, point out the headings Track and Field in the table.
16	$a = 89°$ $b = 28°$ $c = 55°$ $d = 120°$		max. 4 marks	
17	**a** USA Spain Greece Portugal France	3 24 6 3 12	max. 2 marks	2 marks for all correct, 1 mark for 3 or more correct.
	b Angles of pie chart must measure: London Paris Rome Athens New York	 90° 120° 60° 50° 40°	max. 2 marks	2 marks for all sectors of the pie chart correctly sized, 1 mark for 3 or more correct.

Paper 3: reasoning

Record the mark awarded for each question. Half marks cannot be awarded.

Question	Requirement	Mark	Additional guidance
1	24	1 mark	If the child incorrectly answered 26 or 20 or 18, they are counting the parts of the cubes that are visible. Encourage the child to think of this as a 3-D shape and to count each layer and the number of layers altogether.
2	Test 1: 62.5% Test 2: 65%	1 mark	Give the mark only if both answers are correct. These answers can be found by: • (Test 1) dividing 50 by 80 and multiplying by 100 • (Test 2) dividing 26 by 40 and multiplying by 100
3	3.14, 3.146, 3.4, 3.42	1 mark	If the child gave the incorrect answer 3.4, 3.14, 3.42 and 3.146, they do not yet fully understand the nature of decimals. The number of digits of a decimal does not determine its size.
4	a –2°C	1 mark	Counting back 9°C from 9°C will bring you to zero. Counting back 11°C from 9°C will take you to –2°C.
	b 4°C	1 mark	Counting on 8°C from –8°C will bring you to zero. Counting on 12°C from –8°C will take you to 4°C.
5	£7.63	2 marks	Give 2 marks for the correct answer. Give one mark if the answer is incorrect but an attempt has been made *either* to subtract £5 from £87.49 and then to subtract £74.86 from the answer *or* to add £5 to £74.86 and then to subtract the answer from £87.49.
6	a 32	1 mark	Give 1 mark for answers between 31 and 33 inclusive.
	b 22	1 mark	Give 1 mark for answers between 21 and 23 inclusive.
	c Yes *and* a valid explanation	1 mark	Discuss with the child that the information shown on the graph only shows the visitor numbers 'on the hour' (for example at 9:00, 10:00, 11:00 and so on), *and* that between these hours we don't know how many people were in the castle. For example, between 14:00 and 15:00 there may have been more than 50 visitors.

Question	Requirement	Mark	Additional guidance
7	**a** £1 or £1.00	1 mark	Here the child is required to know that 400g is four-tenths or two-fifths of 1kg. They then need to find four-tenths or two-fifths of £2.50. One-fifth is £2.50 ÷ 5 = 50p, so two-fifths is 50p × 2 = £1. Money answers must be written correctly for questions of this type. Amounts of money should never be written with both the **£** sign and a **p** sign.
	b 125g	max. 2 marks	Encourage the child to change the amounts of money so that they are either in pounds or in pence, rather than a mixture of the two. 60p is one-eighth of 480p. So one-eighth of 1kg (1000g) is 1000g ÷ 8 = 125g. Award 1 mark if there has been some attempt to divide £4.80 by 60p or to find one-eighth of 1kg.
8	**a** 12	1 mark	He uses 12 red tins and 4 white tins.
	b 28	1 mark	He mixed 20 red tins and 8 white tins, making 28 tins altogether.
9	20.8cm	1 mark	
10	3	1 mark	
11	**a** 9	1 mark	9 is a factor of 108, a multiple of 3 and a square number.
	b 23	1 mark	23 is prime and 2 + 3 = 5.
12	A = 64 B = 16	1 mark	Only give a mark if both answers are correct and the right way round, so do *not* give the mark for the answer A = 16, B = 64.
13	$\frac{2}{3}$ and $\frac{6}{9}$ *or* $\frac{3}{9}$ and $\frac{2}{6}$	1 mark	The fractions can be in any order, for example $\frac{6}{9}$ and $\frac{2}{3}$ *or* $\frac{2}{6}$ and $\frac{3}{9}$.
14	15, 23, 31	1 mark	All numbers must be correct. The sequence goes up in steps of 8.
15	9	1 mark	For the mean to be 7, the total must be 7 × 5 = 35. The total of the four visible numbers is 26, so the fifth card must be 9.
16	**a** (3,1)	1 mark	The phrase 'along the corridor and up or down the stairs' can help to remind the child that the first co-ordinate, for example −3, means across 3 to the left, and the second co-ordinate, for example 2, means 2 up.
	b	1 mark	
17	**a** D	1 mark	D is a pentagon.
	b A	1 mark	A is a parallelogram.
	c C	1 mark	C has a diagonal line of symmetry.

Question	Requirement	Mark	Additional guidance
18	$y - 9$	1 mark	
19	3	1 mark	3 Laser rides = £7.80, leaving £6.75, which must be 3 Mars rides and 1 Star ride.
20	a Any two different numbers that multiply to make 48, for example 24 and 2.	1 mark	Note that 12 × 4 is not acceptable as all numbers must be different.
	b Any two different numbers that divide to make 7.	1 mark	Answers could include 14 ÷ 2, 21 ÷ 3, 28 ÷ 4, 35 ÷ 5, 42 ÷ 6. Note that 7 ÷ 1 and 49 ÷ 7 are not acceptable (see above).
	c Any numbers that make this correct, for example 4 and 2, 10 and 1.	1 mark	
21	a 4.5m	1 mark	Do not give a mark for the answer 450 as this is not given in metres.
	b 3.4m	1 mark	Do not give a mark for the answer 340 as this is not given in metres.